WOULD YOU RATHER?

Gross Kids Only

Sick Scenarios for Kids Age 8

8

Year Old Edition

Try Not To Laugh
Challenge®
BONUS PLAY

Join our Joke Club and get the Bonus Play PDF!

Simply send us an email to:

 **TNTLPublishing@gmail.com**

and you will get the following:

- **10 Hilarious Would You Rather Questions**
- **An entry in our Monthly Giveaway of a $50 Amazon Gift card!**

We draw a new winner each month and will contact you via email!

Good luck!

Welcome to
The Try Not to Laugh Challenge®
Would You Rather?
GROSS EDITION

RULES:

• Face your opponent and decide who is Player 1 and Player 2.

• Starting with Player 1, read the Would You Rather question aloud and pick an answer. The same player will then explain why they chose that answer in the most hilarious or wacky way possible!

• If the reason makes Player 2 laugh, then a laugh point is scored!

• Take turns going back and forth, then mark your total laugh points at the end of each round!

• Whoever gets the most laugh points is officially crowned the Gross Laugh Master!

• If ending with a tie, finish with the Tie-Breaker round for WINNER TAKES ALL!

Most importantly, have fun and be SILLY!

REMEMBER, these scenarios listed in the book are solely for fun and games! Please do <u>NOT</u> attempt any of the crazy scenarios in this book.

ROUND

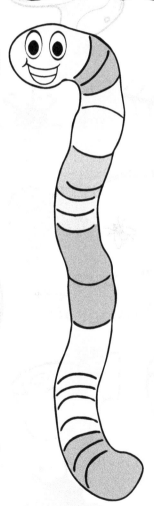

PLAYER 1

Would you rather eat 5 large chocolate-covered roaches OR 50 small sautéed crickets?

Laugh Point_____/1

Would you rather have to wear a diaper outside your pants for one day, OR wear your underwear on your head for one day?

Laugh Point_____/1

PLAYER 1

(DON'T FORGET TO EXPLAIN YOUR ANSWERS!)

Would you rather win an award for World's Loudest Burp OR win an award for World's Longest Booger?

Laugh Point_____ /1

Would you rather wake up one morning with tiny wings OR huge antlers?

Laugh Point_____ /1

PASS THE BOOK TO PLAYER 2!

PLAYER 2

Would you rather eat a bowl of soggy boogers **OR** a plate of crunchy toenails?

Laugh Point_____/1

Would you rather wear your choice of clothes, but they're always dirty **OR** have only one clean outfit to wear, every day?

Laugh Point_____/1

PLAYER 2

Would you rather be an ogre with bad breath OR an elf with floppy ears?

Laugh Point_____/1

Would you rather have angel wings that opened whenever you smiled, OR dragon wings that burst open when you were angry?

Laugh Point_____/1

TIME TO SCORE YOUR POINTS! →

PLAYER 1

/4

ROUND TOTAL

PLAYER 2

/4

ROUND TOTAL

ROUND WINNER

ROUND

PLAYER 1

Would you rather have to smell rotten food all day OR smell the spray of a skunk all night?

Laugh Point____ /1

Would you rather have snot-filled jelly donuts OR chocolate brownies made out of dog poop?

Laugh Point____ /1

14

PLAYER 1

Would you rather walk on your hands across a field of sticky marshmallows OR skip through a river of jello?

Laugh Point_____/1

Would you rather constantly feel like you're going to sneeze, but never sneeze OR constantly sneeze?

Laugh Point_____/1

PASS THE BOOK TO PLAYER 2!

15

PLAYER 2

(DON'T FORGET TO EXPLAIN YOUR ANSWERS!)

Would you rather smell your gym coach's stinky sock OR smell a stranger's stinky armpit?

Laugh Point_____/1

Would you rather walk on a carpet made of cockroaches OR swim in a bathtub filled with living worms?

Laugh Point_____/1

PLAYER 2

(DON'T FORGET TO EXPLAIN YOUR ANSWERS!)

Would you rather have a bird pop out of your mouth every hour on the hour (like a human cuckoo clock), OR have to clean your house by sucking up dirt with your mouth (like a human vacuum) for a week?

Laugh Point____ /1

Would you rather travel around the entire Earth by flying OR by sailing?

Laugh Point____ /1

TIME TO SCORE YOUR POINTS! →

17

PLAYER 1

/4

ROUND TOTAL

PLAYER 2

/4

ROUND TOTAL

ROUND WINNER

ROUND

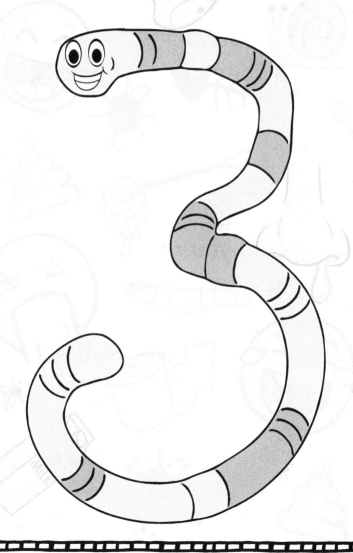

PLAYER 1

Would you rather lick the bottom of your shoe OR lick the toes of an elephant?

Laugh Point_____/1

Would you rather wear a bright purple suit covered in flashing disco sequins, OR an oversized, yellow cowboy hat made from rubber ducks?

Laugh Point_____/1

PLAYER 1

Would you rather break out in purple lumps every time you text your crush,
OR break out in giant green spots every time you give a class presentation?

Laugh Point____/1

Would you rather own an unicorn-filled farm OR a dragon-filled dungeon?

Laugh Point____/1

PASS THE BOOK TO PLAYER 2!

PLAYER 2

(DON'T FORGET TO EXPLAIN YOUR ANSWERS!)

Would you rather be able to bring balloon animals to life, OR bring stuffed animals to life?

Laugh Point____ /1

Would you rather eat a donut that fell into a public garbage can OR eat dip that someone sneezed in?

Laugh Point____ /1

PLAYER 2

Would you rather mow all the grass around your school OR wash all the dishes from your school's cafeteria?

Laugh Point_____ /1

◆

Would you rather have leopard stripes in your hair OR bird feathers for eyebrows?

Laugh Point_____ /1

TIME TO SCORE YOUR POINTS! →

PLAYER 1

/4

ROUND TOTAL

PLAYER 2

/4

ROUND TOTAL

ROUND WINNER

ROUND

PLAYER 1

Would you rather organize 500 books in alphabetical order OR recite the ABCs 20x backwards?

Laugh Point_____ /1

Would you rather be completely covered in mud OR have sand poured into your clothes and shoes?

Laugh Point_____ /1

PLAYER 1

Would you rather have to cut your hair every other day OR never cut it again?

Laugh Point____ /1

Would you rather be able to only communicate through jokes, OR only be able to communicate through Would You Rather questions?

Laugh Point____ /1

PASS THE BOOK TO PLAYER 2!

27

PLAYER 2

If you were allergic to chocolate, would you rather eat it and develop an itchy rash each time OR never eat it again?

Laugh Point_____ /1

Would you rather wear only a diaper in public for one full day OR suck on a pacifier for three days?

Laugh Point_____ /1

PLAYER 2

(DON'T FORGET TO EXPLAIN YOUR ANSWERS!)

Would you rather sneeze sequins OR cough confetti?

Laugh Point____/1

Would you rather have to run through the halls of your school wearing your holey pajamas OR have to wear polka dots painted on your face all day?

Laugh Point____/1

TIME TO SCORE YOUR POINTS! →

29

PLAYER 1

/4

ROUND TOTAL

PLAYER 2

/4

ROUND TOTAL

ROUND WINNER

ROUND

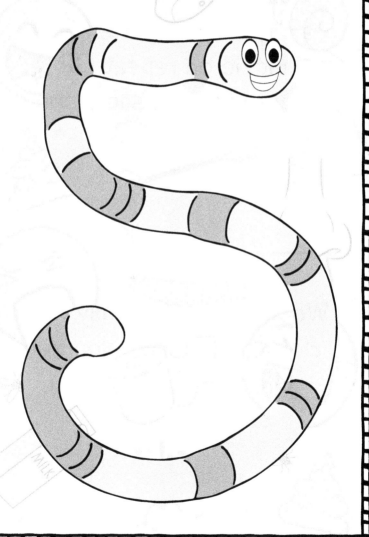

PLAYER 1

(DON'T FORGET TO EXPLAIN YOUR ANSWERS!)

Would you rather spend
a day watching the same
movie on repeat OR
listening to the same song,
non-stop?

Laugh Point_____/1

Would you rather only wear
clothes you made yourself
OR only eat food you
cooked yourself?

Laugh Point_____/1

PLAYER 1

Would you rather go to the ice cream shop, but not eat OR go to Walt Disney World, but not ride any rides?

Laugh Point____ /1

Would you rather have to eat a friend's boogers OR have to eat your own ear wax?

Laugh Point____ /1

PASS THE BOOK TO PLAYER 2!

PLaYeR 2

Would you rather bake 250 cupcakes for a school picnic the next day, OR have to eat 50 cupcakes all by yourself within 2 hours?

Laugh Point____ /1

Would you rather your job be to heat every volcano with one pot of lava at a time, OR have to refill the ocean with one saltbox at a time?

Laugh Point____ /1

PLaYeR 2

(DON'T FORGET TO EXPLAIN YOUR ANSWERS!)

Would you rather take a bath in chunky, rotten milk OR take a shower in hot prune juice?

Laugh Point_____ /1

Would you rather wear a swimsuit in the South Pole during a snowstorm, OR a winter coat in the Sahara Desert during summer?

Laugh Point_____ /1

TIME TO SCORE YOUR POINTS! →

PLAYER 1

/4

ROUND TOTAL

PLAYER 2

/4

ROUND TOTAL

ROUND WINNER

ROUND

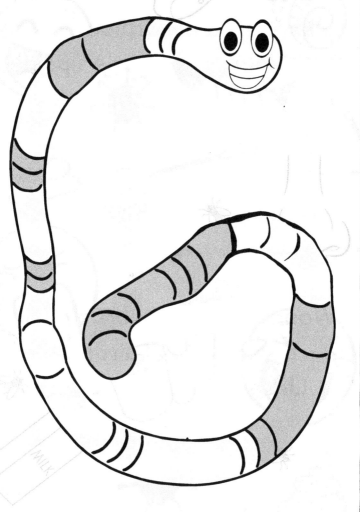

Would you rather cross a shark tank blindfolded on a tightrope, OR dangle upside down from a helicopter over the ocean?

Laugh Point_____/1

Would you rather brush your teeth with a hairbrush OR brush your hair with a toothbrush?

Laugh Point_____/1

PLAYER 1

Would you rather your skin be made out of solid steel OR finely carved wood?

Laugh Point_____ /1

Would you rather walk across a frozen pond without shoes OR play in the snow wearing only a swimsuit?

Laugh Point_____ /1

PASS THE BOOK TO PLAYER 2!

PLAYER 2

(DON'T FORGET TO EXPLAIN YOUR ANSWERS!)

Would you rather live 300 years in the past as royalty, OR live 300 years in the future as an everyday person?

Laugh Point____ /1

Would you rather perform a whistling solo in a talent competition, while gurgling Pop Rocks OR perform a dance solo, while you are stomping grapes?

Laugh Point____ /1

PLAYER 2

(DON'T FORGET TO EXPLAIN YOUR ANSWERS!)

Would you rather give up all video games for two years, OR lose all holidays and your birthday for a year?

Laugh Point____ /1

Would you rather only be able to fly by spinning really fast OR move through walls, but only if you run straight at them?

Laugh Point____ /1

TIME TO SCORE YOUR POINTS! →

PLAYER 1

/4
ROUND TOTAL

PLAYER 2

/4
ROUND TOTAL

ROUND
WINNER

ROUND

PLAYER 1

(DON'T FORGET TO EXPLAIN YOUR ANSWERS!)

Would you rather have your feet glued to the ground for a day OR have your hands glued to the ceiling for 12 hours?

Laugh Point_____ /1

Would you rather do homework every night OR do your parents' chores every night, for a month straight?

Laugh Point_____ /1

PLAYER 1

Would you rather always get lost whenever you went to a store OR always forget what you came to buy?

Laugh Point____ /1

Would you rather always be hungry, but can only eat dirt OR always be thirsty, but can only drink soapy water?

Laugh Point____ /1

PASS THE BOOK TO PLAYER 2!

45

PLAYER 2

(DON'T FORGET TO EXPLAIN YOUR ANSWERS!)

Would you rather have the ability to breathe fire **OR** hold your breath underwater for 30 minutes?

Laugh Point_____ /1

Would you rather be adopted by a family of giants **OR** join a family of dwarves?

Laugh Point_____ /1

PLAYER 2

(DON'T FORGET TO EXPLAIN YOUR ANSWERS!)

Would you rather touch your grandpa's sweaty armpit OR rub your grandma's feet after a long day in the sun?

Laugh Point____ /1

Would you rather eat a giant, hot pepper-flavored sundae OR a huge, raw egg and spinach milkshake?

Laugh Point____ /1

TIME TO SCORE YOUR POINTS! →

47

PLAYER 1

/4

ROUND TOTAL

PLAYER 2

/4

ROUND TOTAL

ROUND WINNER

ROUND

PLAYER 1

(DON'T FORGET TO EXPLAIN YOUR ANSWERS!)

Would you rather only eat dog food for a week OR only eat baby food for a month?

Laugh Point_____ /1

Would you rather snore loud enough for your neighbors to hear you, OR fart loudly every time you blink?

Laugh Point_____ /1

PLAYER 1

Would you rather eat a lollipop covered in dog fur OR a chocolate-covered worm?

Laugh Point____ /1

Would you rather have purple polka dots all over your body OR be striped like a zebra?

Laugh Point____ /1

PASS THE BOOK TO PLAYER 2!

PLAYER 2

Would you rather be fed regurgitated food like a baby bird, OR live in a nest made of dirty grass and garbage from around the neighborhood?

Laugh Point_____/1

Would you rather get a paper cut on every finger daily OR slam your big toe into a dresser daily?

Laugh Point_____/1

PLAYER 2

Would you rather drink someone else's snot OR eat someone else's toenails?

Laugh Point____/1

Would you rather finish a partially eaten meal you found at a restaurant, OR finish a drink in a cup you found at the beach?

Laugh Point____/1

TIME TO SCORE YOUR POINTS! →

PLAYER 1

/4

ROUND TOTAL

PLAYER 2

/4

ROUND TOTAL

ROUND
WINNER

ROUND

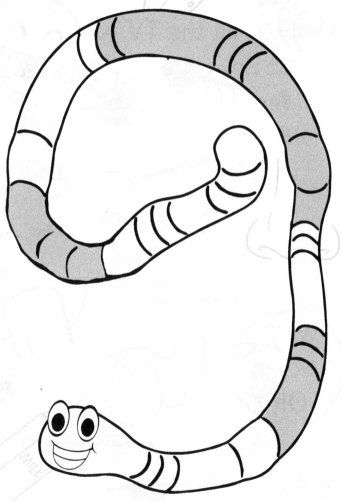

PLAYER 1

(DON'T FORGET TO EXPLAIN YOUR ANSWERS!)

Would you rather be able to watch all the TV you want, but never be able to play video games again OR play video games, but never be able to watch TV again?

Laugh Point_____ /1

Would you rather have your bottom where your nose is OR your nose where your bottom is?

Laugh Point_____ /1

PLAYER 1

(DON'T FORGET TO EXPLAIN YOUR ANSWERS!)

Would you rather have cooked noodles for fingers OR raw chicken nuggets for toes?

Laugh Point_____/1

Would you rather trip over your own feet constantly OR shed hair all over the sofa, as the dogs do?

Laugh Point_____/1

PASS THE BOOK TO PLAYER 2!

PLAYER 2

(DON'T FORGET TO EXPLAIN YOUR ANSWERS!)

Would you rather wear a rainbow wig all day **OR** googly eye sunglasses all night?

Laugh Point_____ /1

Would you rather find spiders in your backpack **OR** worms in your lunch box?

Laugh Point_____ /1

58

PLAYER 2

(DON'T FORGET TO EXPLAIN YOUR ANSWERS!)

Would you rather have to get upstairs by climbing a ladder with broken steps, OR go downstairs by riding down a slide with alligators at the bottom?

Laugh Point_____/1

Would you rather make a sculpture out of ice cubes OR create a picture out of trash?

Laugh Point_____/1

TIME TO SCORE YOUR POINTS! →

PLAYER 1

/4

ROUND TOTAL

PLAYER 2

/4

ROUND TOTAL

ROUND
WINNER

ROUND

PLAYER 1

Would you rather have to jump everywhere like a frog, OR have to run everywhere like a cheetah?

Laugh Point_____ /1

Would you rather have X-ray vision OR the ability to hypnotize people?

Laugh Point_____ /1

PLAYER 1

Would you rather be stuck living the rest of your life as a five-year-old OR your grandparents' age?

Laugh Point____ /1

Would you rather only have cold showers OR only have warm drinks?

Laugh Point____ /1

PASS THE BOOK TO PLAYER 2!

63

PLAYER 2

Would you rather eat salty peanuts with no teeth OR drink a milkshake without using your hands?

Laugh Point_____/1

Would you rather have to find out that your sibling's scab collection was in the cereal box the hard way, OR find a half of a worm in your apple while eating it?

Laugh Point_____/1

PLaYeR 2

(DON'T FORGET TO EXPLAIN YOUR ANSWERS!)

Would you rather have to drag a heavy, metal ball chained to your ankle everywhere, OR do five push-ups for every ten steps you take?

Laugh Point____/1

Would you rather lose all your teeth OR all your hair?

Laugh Point____/1

TIME TO SCORE YOUR POINTS! →

PLAYER 1

/4
ROUND TOTAL

PLAYER 2

/4
ROUND TOTAL

ROUND WINNER

ADD UP ALL YOUR POINTS FROM EACH ROUND.
THE PLAYER WITH THE MOST POINTS IS
CROWNED

THE GROSS LAUGH MASTER!

IN THE EVENT OF A TIE, CONTINUE TO
ROUND 11 FOR THE TIE-BREAKER!

PLaYeR 1 _____
GRAND TOTAL

PLaYeR 2 _____
GRAND TOTAL

_____

★ THE GROSS
★ LAUGH MASTER ★

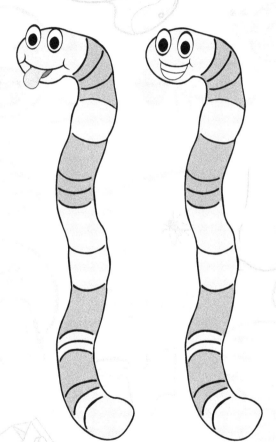

ROUND

TIE-BREAKER
(WINNER TAKES ALL!)

PLAYER 1

Would you rather sneeze every time you lie OR yawn every time you have to apologize?

Laugh Point____ /1

Would you rather be able to solve any math problem in your head, OR be able to spell any word without looking it up?

Laugh Point____ /1

PLAYER 1

(DON'T FORGET TO EXPLAIN YOUR ANSWERS!)

Would you rather have to walk up steep hills to get everywhere **OR** walk everywhere with bare feet?

Laugh Point_____ /1

Would you rather have a wooden leg **OR** have wooden teeth that put splinters in your lips?

Laugh Point_____ /1

PASS THE BOOK TO PLAYER 2!

PLAYER 2

Would you rather have the longest tongue OR the biggest ears, in the world?

Laugh Point____/1

Would you rather have the ability to glow in the dark OR camouflage into your surroundings?

Laugh Point____/1

PLAYER 2

Would you rather be deathly terrified of your own skin OR be terrified of your own hair (body hair included)?

Laugh Point____ /1

Would you rather wear an outfit made of dead fish OR have to wear a wig made of living worms?

Laugh Point____ /1

TIME TO SCORE YOUR POINTS! →

ADD UP ALL YOUR POINTS FROM ROUND 11.
THE PLAYER WITH THE MOST POINTS IS CROWNED
THE GROSS LAUGH MASTER!

PLAYER 1

/4

_____
ROUND TOTAL

PLAYER 2

/4

_____
ROUND TOTAL

_____

THE GROSS LAUGH MASTER

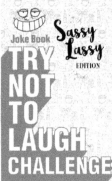

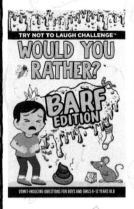

OTHER JOKE BOOKS!

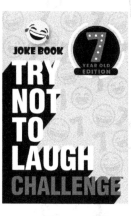 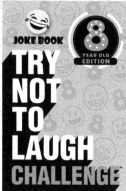 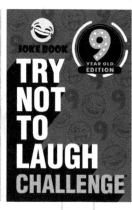

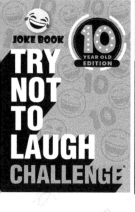 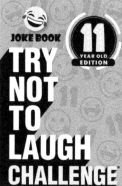 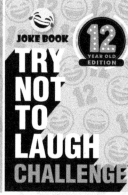

IF YOU HAVE ENJOYED OUR BOOK, WE WOULD LOVE FOR YOU TO REVIEW US ON AMAZON!

CPSIA information can be obtained
at www.ICGtesting.com
Printed in the USA
LVHW051035050222
710245LV00011B/245

9 781649 430489